With love to you both
from   Anne
Jan '89

Joyce Grenfell was born Joyce Phipps, daughter of the youngest of the beautiful American Langhorne sisters, of whom the most celebrated was Nancy, Lady Astor.

Her girlhood, spent on the fringes of the famous Cliveden set among such men as George Bernard Shaw and Noel Coward, spanned the twenties, but it was not until 1938, at a dinner party, that she gave an impromptu imitation of a Women's Institute speaker and discovered her genius for dramatic monologue.

These Nursery School sketches are perennial favourites in her repertoire and have entertained millions.

Also by Joyce Grenfell

JOYCE GRENFELL REQUESTS THE PLEASURE
STATELY AS A GALLEON
TURN BACK THE CLOCK
IN PLEASANT PLACES
AN INVISIBLE FRIENDSHIP
JOYCE, BY HERSELF AND HER FRIENDS

George – Don't Do That ...

Six Nursery School Sketches

and

'Writer of Children's Books'

BY

Joyce Grenfell

ILLUSTRATED BY

John Ward

Futura

A Futura Book

First published in Great Britain by
Macmillan London Limited in 1977

First Futura Publications edition 1978
4th printing 1982
Reprinted 1984, 1987, 1988

ISBN 0 7088 1479 4

Filmset in Monophoto Ehrhardt 13 on 15pt and
Reproduced, printed and bound in Great Britain by
Hazell Watson & Viney Limited
Member of BPCC plc
Aylesbury, Bucks, England

Futura Publications
A Division of
Macdonald & Co (Publishers) Ltd
66–73 Shoe Lane
London EC4P 4AB
A member of Maxwell Pergamon Publishing Corporation plc

To all who cope
in Nursery Schools

Contents

Foreword

The original idea for the Nursery School sketches began in a radio series, the 'How' programmes: a collaboration between Stephen Potter and myself. In 1944 we produced 'How to talk to children', and in it was the first brief draft of what later turned into a full-length sketch called 'Flowers'.

I had never been in a Nursery School, but I was always aware that most of us change our manner and our tone of voice when we speak to infants. Try saying to a very small child: 'Who's got beautiful new blue shoes on!' and I think you will find that you have put on a special voice that you would not use to talk to people of your own size.

My father was the only person I ever knew who addressed babies in prams as if they were his contemporaries. He spoke as he would to a

He spoke as he would to a bank manager.

bank manager or a bishop; friendly but respectful. I never saw a baby turn away or wince. Sometimes a tiny eyebrow may have been raised, but a look of interest took over and the pleasing pink blob of a small face registered relief and rapport.

Even as a child I noticed the way those in authority spoke to the rest of us, and I could reproduce it to amuse my fellows. I marked the sarcastic note that one teacher relied on. She was surface-jolly, had favourites and her sarcasm had bite. I observed this with some disdain. You couldn't trust Mrs Bowthorne to

Mrs Bowthorne and Miss Chugwell.

be fair. Miss Chugwell, more secure in her relationships, drew from her class of eight-year-olds a readier, more generous response. She didn't need weapons to buoy up her ego. She spoke low, without pleading.

Children's toys, games and clothes, hair-styles and language change; so do their names – Wendys, Pixys, Nevilles and Normans have currently given way to Shirleens, Sandras, Rocks and Waynes, but their unpredictable observations, discoveries and individualities, continue, thank heaven, to surprise, confound and delight.

Talking to three-to-five-year-olds presents different problems, but as far as I can see authority's voice is still what it always was: bright, bluffingly calm, cheerful, encouraging and occasionally desperate. It is that bright teacher-tone of voice that needs to be added to the printed word of this collection of scripts.

For the script of 'A Writer of Children's Books' please hear a tone less desperate and wholly confident – her sales are astronomical. She is unaware that what she writes is not Eng. Lit.

John Ward's drawings are not portraits of Sidney, George, Hazel, Susan and the rest. None of them is identified, but their kind is.

Joyce Grenfell

1977

NURSERY SCHOOL SKETCHES

NATIVITY
Play

Hello, Mrs Binton. I'm so glad you could get along to see a rehearsal of our Nativity Play! Can you squeeze in there? I'm afraid our chairs are a wee bitty wee, as they say north of the border!

Now then, children. We are going to start our rehearsal. Where are my Mary and Joseph?

Mary and Joseph were friends.

That's right, Shirleen, take Denis by the hand and come sit nice and quietly on this bench in the middle.

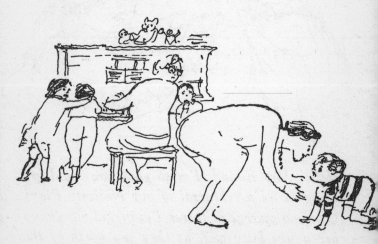

Oh, you're a cattle, are you?

Don't drag him. He'll come if you leave him alone!

Don't hit each other, Mary and Joseph were *friends*.

Now, who are my Wise Men?

You're a Wise Man, aren't you, Geoffrey?

Oh, aren't you? What are you then?

Oh, you're a cattle, are you? And you are going to low. Splendid! Go over to Miss Boulting, will you, please?

Miss Boulting ... You are organising the animals and the angels? He is one of yours.

Now, my Wise Men here, please!

Billy, Peter and George.

And George, Wise Men never do that ...

Now my Kings, please.

Of course, Mrs Binton, we know that by tradition the Wise Men and the Kings are one and the same, but we did want everyone in our Nursery School Nativity Play to have a chance, so we have taken a few liberties, and I don't think any one will mind.

Now Kings: Sidney, Neville, Cliff and Nikolas Anoniodes.

Four Kings, I'm afraid. We happen to have four lovely crowns, so it seemed a pity not to use them.

Sidney, put your crown on *straight* please, not over one eye. What have you got under your jersey?

What have you got under your jersey?

That's not the place for a hamster, is it. Put him straight back in his little pen, please.

Sidney, which one have you got, Paddington or Harold Wilson?

Well, who's got Paddington?

Neville, put him back at once.

Poor Paddington and Harold Wilson, it isn't very Christmassy for them under your jersey.

Sidney, I think it serves you right if Harold Wilson bit you, and don't bite him back.

Because he's smaller than you are. Are you bleeding?

Then don't make such a fuss.

Cliff, put your crown on, please.

It's too big? Let's see. Ah, yes it is . . .

Where are you! Oh, there you are! Nice to see you again! Change with Nikolas.

Nikolas, you can manage a big crown, can't you? You've got just the ears for it.

I think if you pull your ears down a bit that will hold it up. And lean back a bit. That's it.

Stay like that, dear. Don't move.

Wise Men and Kings, don't muddle yourselves with each other.

Now then, Shepherds.

Jimmy, you are my First Shepherd and not a racing car.

Yes, Caroline, you're a shepherd.

No, dear you can't wear your Little Bo-Peep costume: because there aren't any little girl shepherdesses in our play. They're all boy

Little Bo-Peep.

shepherds, and you are a girl being a boy shepherd.

Yes, it is rotten. But we just have to settle for it. I think if you are very good perhaps you can wear a lovely grey beard; wouldn't that be fun?

George, what do Wise Men never do?

Yes . . .

Jimmy, do you remember what you see up in the sky? Something lovely, isn't it?

Do you remember what you see up in the sky?

No, not a baby. Try again.

It's a lovely silver star, and you are going to put your hand up and point to it. And what are you going to say when you do that?

No, Sidney, he isn't going to say, 'Please may I go to the bathroom?'

Children, that isn't funny; it's a perfectly

I think perhaps next year we might make do with a Christmas carol.

natural function, and we might as well get used to it.

Come on, Jimmy. You are going to say, 'Behold!' aren't you?

Yes, you are, dear. You said it yesterday.

You'd rather say it tomorrow?

Perhaps you are right.

We have broken the back of the play, so you may as well get ready to go home. Hand in your crowns gently, please. No, Sidney, you can't wear your crown home on the bus.

I think – I HOPE it will be all right on the night.

But you know, Mrs Binton, I think perhaps next year we might make do with a Christmas carol.

Flowers

Children – we're going to do our nice 'Moving to Music' this morning, so let's make a lovely fairy ring, shall we? And then we'll all be flowers growing in the grass.

Let's make a big circle – spread out – wider – wider – just finger-tips touching – that's it.

Sue, let go of Neville –

Because flowers don't hold hands, they just touch finger-tips.

SUE. Let go of Neville.

And Sue, we don't want GRUMBLERS in our fairy ring, do we? We only want *smilers*.

Yes David, you're a smiler – so is Lavinia – and Peggy and Geoffrey. Yes, you're *all* smilers.

Yes, you're all smilers.

QUIET, PLEASE.

Don't get so excited.

And Sue is going to be a smiler too, aren't you Sue? That's better.

George – don't do that . . .

Now then, let's all put on our Thinking Caps, shall we, and think what flowers we are going to choose to be.

Lavinia? – What flower are you?

A bluebell. Good.

A bluebell. Good.

Peggy?

A red rose. That's nice.

Neville?

A *wild* rose. Well done, Neville!

Sidney? – Sidney, pay attention, dear, and don't pummel Rosemary – what flower are you going to choose to be?

A *horse* isn't a flower, Sidney.

No children, it isn't funny, it's very silly. If Sidney can't think of a better flower than that

Sidney, pay attention, dear.

we'll have to go on to someone else until he can.

Now then Sue, what are you?

Another rose! Oh I *have* got a lovely bunch of roses, haven't I? Peggy is a *red* one and Neville is a *wild* one, so I expect you are a beautiful *white* one, aren't you?

Oh, you're another red one! I see...

Now then Sidney?

A carrot *isn't a flower*, Sidney. *Think* dear, and don't blow like that. How about a tulip?

A holly-leaf isn't a flower, Sidney. All right, you'd better be a holly-leaf.

Now, children, listen very carefully.

Elvis, stop bouncing, please.

No, bouncing isn't dancing, Elvis. Don't

argue, dear – just stop bouncing. You watch the others – you'll see.

When Miss Boulting plays her music I want you all to get up on to your tipmost toes, light as feathers and dance away all over the room wherever the music takes you. And remember: you are all lovely flowers in the grass.

Everybody ready?

Just a minute, Miss Boulting.

Sidney – come here, please.

What have you got in your mouth?

What have you got in your mouth?

33

I can't hear a word you're saying, Sidney, so go out of the room and spit it out, whatever it is, and then come back and tell me what it was. And Sidney. Both feet. Don't hop.

Now then, children, we're not going to wait for a boy who puts things in his mouth like a baby – we're going to be lovely flowers growing in the grass, and the sun is shining down on us to make us grow tall and beautiful and – Geoffrey, stand up – flowers don't look backwards through their legs, do they?

Flowers don't look backwards through their legs.

What flower are you?
A fat daisy! Good.
Hazel, what do we do with our heads?
We hold them up.
I should think so.

34

Come in, Sidney!

COME IN. There's no need to knock the door down, is there?

Now what did you have in your mouth?

It can't have been nothing, Sidney, because I distinctly saw something.

Yes, I know it's nothing *now* but what was it *then*?

A big button! Well, I'm very glad you spat it out, aren't you?

You didn't? Do you feel all right, Sidney? Sure?

Well, get back into your place, then.

Incidentally, where did you get the button?

Off Rosemary's pink frock. I'm ashamed of you, Sidney, a big boy of four to go around eating buttons off little girls' frocks. What flower are you going to be? I've forgotten. You'd better be a hollyhock.

No, you can't be a *super-jet*, and if you are going to be a crosspatch you'd better go and sit down over there till you are a nice boy again. You can be thinking what flower you are going to be. Go along . . .

George — what did I say before? Well, don't . . .

No, you can't be a super-jet.

Come along, children. Listen carefully to the music and then dance like a flower to it.

We're ready at last, Miss Boulting. I'm so sorry.

One – two – Off we go.

Dance, Neville, don't just stand there. Dance.

Head up, Hazel, and use your arms.

Peggy, dear – don't forget to breathe.

Rhythm, George. And cheer up – you're a *happy* flower, George.

Yes, you are.

Because I say so.

Oh good, Sidney, I knew you'd think of something.

All right, you shall be a cauliflower — only be it *gently*.

We're ready at last, Miss Boulting.

Free Activity Period

Oh, hello, Mrs Hingle. I'm so glad you could come along. As you see, we're just having a Free Activity Period, and in our Free Activity Period each little individual chooses his or her own occupation. Some are painting, some are using plasticine, and some work at a sand-table. We feel that each little one must get to the bottom of his or her self and find out what he really wants of life.

39

Who is making that buzzing noise?

Well, stop it please, Neville.

Hazel, dear, come away from the door and get on with your plasticine.

I love to see them so happily occupied, each one expressing his little personality . . .

George – don't do that . . .

Now, children, I want you all to say 'Good morning' to Mrs Hingle. Good morning, Mrs Hingle.

No, Sidney, not good-bye. Mrs Hingle has only just come. You don't want her to go away yet?

No, she hasn't got a funny hat on, that's her hair.

So sorry, Mrs Hingle. Sometimes we ARE just a trifle outspoken. We try to encourage honesty, only sometimes it doesn't always . . .

And this is my friend Caroline, and Caroline is painting such a lovely red picture, aren't you, Caroline? I wonder what it is? Perhaps it's a lovely red sunset, is it? Or a big red orange?

It's a picture of Mummy! For a moment I thought it was a big red orange, but now you tell me, I can see it is a picture of Mummy.

Aren't you going to give her any nose?

Say 'Good morning' to Mrs Hingle.

No nose.
It's so interesting the way they see things.
Sidney, don't blow at Edgar, please.
I know I said you could choose what you
are going to do, but you cannot choose to
blow at Edgar.

Because it isn't a good idea.

41

Yes, I know it makes his hair go up and down, but I don't want you to do it. Now get back to the sand table, there's a good boy.

Yes, there is room, Sue; there's heaps of room. Just move up a bit.

Susan! We *never* bite our friends.

Say you are sorry to Sidney. You needn't kiss him.

No, you needn't hug him. Susan, PUT HIM DOWN.

No fisticuffs, please.

She hasn't made any teeth marks, has she, Sidney?

Well then . . . don't fuss.

Free activity.

42

Sometimes our little egos are on the big side, I'm afraid . . .

Hazel, dear, I don't want to have to say it again: please come away from the door.

Why can't you?

Well, you shouldn't have put your finger in the keyhole, and then it wouldn't have got stuck.

Children, there is no need for everyone to come and have a look just because poor Hazel has caught her finger in the keyhole. Back to your work, please.

No, Sidney, I don't think it is stuck in there for ever and ever.

I don't for one minute think we will have to get the Fire Brigade to come and take the door down to set her free. You do exaggerate, Sidney.

Well, if we haven't got her finger out by dinner-time she'll have to have it here.

And her tea.

And her supper and stay the night.

But we are going to get it out, aren't we, Hazel?

David. Turn round, please, David. Right round.

Use your hanky, please, David.

And again.
And again.
And now wipe.

And now wipe.

Thank you, David.

Hazel, why did you put your finger in the keyhole?

To see if it would go in!

Well, now let's see if we can get it out!

Who is making that buzzing noise?

Neville.

I know you are a busy bee, but boy busy-bees don't buzz. Only bee busy-bees buzz.

I can still hear you, Neville.

Neville!

I should think so.

He's such a musical child, and one doesn't want to discourage him.

Sidney, take that paint-brush out of your ear and give it back to Lavinia.

Yes, you do want it back, Lavinia. You like painting.

Yes, you do.

We're hoping she is going to take to it soon.

Now then, Hazel, have you tried wiggling it?

You know, Mrs Hingle, this child's finger really is caught in the keyhole ... I think the

This child's finger really is caught in the keyhole.

*Fire Brigade are the best in an emergency. Yes,
there is a telephone – at the end of the passage.
Would you? Oh, that is good of you. I'll stay
here and hold the fort and prepare the children.
Thank you so much.*

Children, I don't want anyone to get excited, but kind Mrs Hingle has gone to see if
we can get one of those clever men from the
Fire Brigade to come and help us get Hazel's
finger out . . .

Oh, you've got it out, Hazel. Well done.
That's lovely.

*IT'S ALL RIGHT, MRS HINGLE –
SHE'S GOT IT OUT.*

Sidney. You are not to go near that keyhole.

SIDNEY.

Can you get it out?

*I SPOKE TOO SOON, MRS
HINGLE . . .*

Oh, Sidney . . .

Story Time

Children . . . pay attention, please. Free time is over, so put away your things and we are going to tell our nice story, so come over here and make a circle on the floor all around me, and we'll tell the story together. We've got a visitor today, so we can tell our story to her.

49

Will you be all right there, Mrs Binton? I think you'll get a good view of the proceedings.

Hurry up everybody. Don't push – there's lots of room for us all.

This group story-telling is quite a feature of our work here in the Nursery School, Mrs Binton. We like to feel that each little individual has a contribution to make to the world of make-believe, and of course many valuable lessons can be learned from team work. We're a happy band of brothers here!

Edgar, let go of Timmy's ear and settle down.

Come along, everybody.

Sidney, come out from under the table and join in the fun.

No, you're not in a space rocket.

You can't wait for the count-down, you come out now.

Don't you want to help us tell our nice story, Sidney?

Then say, 'No, thank you.' And stop machine-gunning everybody, please.

And Neville, stop being a train and sit down.

All right then, get into the station and then sit down.

And stop machine-gunning everybody, please.

George . . .

No . . .

Let's have some nice straight backs, shall we? What shall we tell our story about today?

Rachel, take your shoe off your head and put it on your foot.

Shall we tell it about a little mouse?

Or a big red bus?

About a dear little bunny rabbit! All right,

Peggy, we'll tell it about a dear little bunny rabbit.

No, Sidney, he wasn't a cowboy bunny rabbit, and he didn't have a gun.

Why don't you come out from under the table and help us tell our nice story?

All right, stay where you are, but you must stop machine-gunning everybody. I don't want to have to tell you again.

One of our individualists! He does have little personality problems, of aggression, but we feel that when his energies are canalised in the right direction he is going to be a quite worthwhile person. That's what we hope . . .

Where did our bunny rabbit live?

No, he didn't live in a TV set.

No, not in a tree.

No, not in a flat.

Think please.

He lived in a HOLE.

Yes, Hazel, of course he did.

Only some of us call it a burrow, don't we?

He lived in a burrow with — who? His mummy bunny rabbit . . . and his? . . . Daddy bunny rabbit . . . and all his? . . . dear little sister and brother bunny rabbits. Wasn't that nice.

Yes, it was, Sidney.

No, Sidney, he wasn't a burglar bunny rabbit. Nor was his daddy. He was just an ordinary businessman bunny rabbit.

David, don't wander away like that.

Yes, I know the window is over there, but you don't want to look out of it now. Our story is getting much too exciting. Come and sit down by Neville.

Neville, don't pull your jersey down over your knees like that; you'll get it all out of shape.

Geoffrey, Lavinia, don't copy him. I don't want everybody pulling their sweaters down over their knees.

I don't want everybody pulling their sweaters down over their knees.

53

Now then, Peggy, you tell us, what was our bunny rabbit's name?

Yes, I know his name was bunny rabbit, but what did his mummy call him, I wonder?

Well, Piggy bunny isn't a very good name for a bunny rabbit. You see a piggy is a piggy and a bunny is a bunny, so we can't have a piggy bunny, can we?

Nor a pussy bunny.

Nor a doggie bunny.

Nor an elephant bunny.

Let's be sensible, please.

No, Sidney, Silly Old Fat Man isn't a good name for a bunny rabbit.

Nor is Wizzle Wuzzle.

No, it's not as funny as all that. There's no need to roll about on the floor.

Timmy, what have you got in your hand?

But we haven't had toast and marmalade for two days. Where did you find it?

In your pocket. No you can't eat it – it's all fuzzy. Now don't touch anything. Go and put it in the waste-paper basket and then wash your hands.

Peggy open the door for him. *Don't touch anything* and hurry back, please; we need you.

Timmy, what have you got in your hand?

Now then, Hazel, what would you like our bunny rabbit to be called?

Yes, I think Princess Anne is a very pretty name, but I don't think it's a very good name for a boy bunny rabbit. We'll call him Billy Bunny Rabbit . . .

Because that's his name . . .

Well, because I happen to know. We're not going to discuss it any more.

Sue don't kiss Neville like that.

Because he doesn't like it.

Yes, I know you like it, but he doesn't.

I don't know why he doesn't like it, but he doesn't.

55

No, and you can't go under the table and kiss Sidney, because he doesn't like it either.

Well, you didn't like it yesterday, Sidney. You must learn to make up your mind, mustn't you?

George . . .

Lavinia, you tell us what our bunny rabbit was doing all day.

He was riding a horse, was he? That is unusual for a rabbit, isn't it? I expect he went gallopy-gallopy, don't you.

Oh good, Sidney, you are coming out to help us tell . . . no, Sidney, you cannot go gallopy-gallopy . . .

Neville, Susan, Peggy . . . everybody . . . come back here at once. You cannot go gallopy . . .

Sidney, come back here.

You know, sometimes I don't think love is enough with children.

You cannot go gallopy-gallopy.

Sing-Song Time

Children, we've had our run around the classroom, and now it's time to start our day's work. We're going to have a sing-song together, and Miss Boulting is going to play for us, so come and settle down over here, please.

Kenny, why haven't you taken your coat off?

No, it isn't time to go home yet, Kenny!
You've only just come.

You'd rather go home? Bad luck.

No, you can't go, not quite yet.

Kenny, you've only been here about ten
minutes. Come and sit on the floor next to
Susan. You like Susan.

No, Susan, I don't think he wants to sit on
your lap.

No, Susan, I don't think he wants to sit on
your lap.

No, I thought he didn't.

Kenny! We don't want to see your tongue, thank you.

No, not even a little bit of it. Put it back, please.

All of it.

And give your jacket to Caroline, I'm sure she'll hang it up for you.

Thank you, Caroline.

Who is that whistling?

Sidney, you know we never whistle indoors. You can whistle in the garden, but we never whistle indoors.

Yes, I know you have just whistled indoors, but don't do it any more.

And don't punch Jacqueline.

I'm sure she didn't say she liked you punching her, did you Jacqueline?

Well, I don't think it's a good idea, so we won't have any more punching.

He is rather a disruptive element in our midst, Miss Boulting, but he does try to belong more than he used to, so we are encouraged, bless his heart.

Let's be *kind* to each other today, shall we? We are going to learn some more of the Drum Marching Song we began yesterday.

61

Drum Marching Song.

Who remembers how it starts?

No, David, it doesn't begin 'Twinkle, Twinkle Little Star'. That's another song.

Yes, I know you know it, but we aren't going to sing it now.

No. Not today.

And not tomorrow.

I don't know when.

We are going to sing our Drum Marching Song now.

Edgar and Neville, why are you standing on those chairs?

You can see into the fish-tank perfectly well from the floor. Get down, please.

No, Neville, you can't hold a fish in your hand.

Because fishes don't like being held in people's hands. They don't like coming out of the water, you see. Their home is in the water.

Well, they do have to come out of the water when we eat them, but these aren't *eating*

Fishes don't like being held in people's hands.

63

fishes. These are *friend* fishes. It's Phyllis and Fred. We wouldn't want to eat Phyllis and Fred.

No, Sidney, you wouldn't.

I don't think they'd be better than sausages.

Come back, please. You don't have to go and see Phyllis and Fred. You know them perfectly well.

I don't know what they are doing behind the weeds, Sidney. Just having a nice friendly game, I expect.

Neville, you tell us how the Drum Marching Song begins.

Yes! That's right.

'Rum tum tum, says the big bass drum'. Well remembered, Neville.

When we know the song well we're going to march to the Drum Song. But today we'll just stand and sing it; so, everybody *ready*?

'Rum tum tum, says the big bass drum.'

Just a minute, Miss Boulting.

Where is your drum, Kenny? No, not on your head. It's in front, isn't it, on a make-believe string round your neck.

Sidney, I heard what you said. You know it isn't 'Rum tum tummy'.

64

It may be funnier, but it isn't right.

Yes, it is a funny joke. Let's get the laughter over, please.

Finished?

Now then. Ready?

Thank you, Miss Boulting.

'Rum tum tummy . . .'

Yes, I made a mistake. It was silly, of me, wasn't it? Yes, very silly.

Sh – sh –. It wasn't as silly as all that.

I think we'll go on to the next bit perhaps . . .

Miss Boulting . . .

'Rooti-toot-toot, says the . . .'

Who says 'Rooti-toot-toot', David?

No, David, not 'Twinkle Twinkle'.

Yes, Lavinia, the '*Cheerful* Flute'.

And what is a flute?

No, Dicky, it isn't an orange.

It isn't a banana.

It isn't an apple.

It isn't FRUIT, it's FLUTE.

FLUTE.

And what is a flute?

Yes, Lavinia, it's in a band. It's a musical instrument in a band. And how do we play it?

No, we don't kick it and bash it about,
Sidney.

Now think.

We *blow* it.

Yes, Edgar, we *blow* it, and the music
comes out of it. It's a musical instrument, and
we *blow* down it.

Rachel, don't blow at Timmy.

Timmy, don't blow back.

And Timmy, don't blow back.

I'm sorry she blew you a very wet one. But
don't blow a wet one back.

Now use your hankies, and wipe each other down, both of you. I'm sure you're both sorry.

No, Kenny, it isn't time to go home yet.

Shirleen, why are you taking your skirt off?

I'm sure Mummy wants you to keep it nice and clean, but you won't get it dirty from singing, you know.

Yes, it is very pretty.

Yes, and it's got little doggies all over it. Little blue and little pink doggies. Put it on again, please. Yes, your panties are pretty; *and* your vest.

But pull down your skirt now.

George. Remember what I asked you not to do? Well, then . . .

'Rooti-toot-toot, says the cheerful flute.'

Rest.

Sidney, you're whistling again. And if you are going to whistle you must learn to do it properly. You don't just draw in your breath like that, you have to blow in and out.

It's no good saying you bet I can't whistle, because I can. I've been able to whistle for a very long time, but I'm not going to do it now. But I can.

I don't know why I compete with him, Miss Boulting. I really shouldn't.

**Here is Mrs Western with our milk and
biscuits.**

Let's start our Drum Marching Song from the very beginning, shall we?

One, two . . .

What did you say, Miss Boulting?

Already! So it is. Oh, good. And here is Mrs Western with our milk and biscuits.

Get into a nice straight line by the trolley, please.

No, Kenny, it isn't time to go home yet. There is still an hour and a half to go . . .

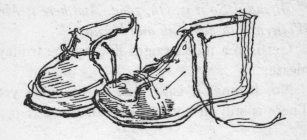

Going Home Time

(*It is winter*)

Children — it's time to go home, so finish tidying up and put on your hats and coats. Some of our mummies are here for us, so hurry up.

Billy won't be long, Mrs Binton. He's on hamster duty.

Now let's see if we can't all help each other.

Janey – I said help each other. Help Bobbie carry that chair, don't pin him against the wall with it.

We're having a go at our good neighbour policy here, Mrs Binton, but it doesn't always . . .

Neville, off the floor, please. Don't lie there.

Don't pin him against the wall with it.

And Sidney, stop painting, please.

Because it's time to go home.

Well, you shouldn't have started another picture, should you. What is it this time?

Another blue man! Oh, I see, so it is.

All right, you can make it just a little bit bluer, but only one more brushful, please, Sidney.

We don't think he's very talented, but we feel it's important to encourage their self-expression. You never know where it might lead . . .

Rachel. Gently – help Teddy *gently* into his coat.

It's a lovely coat, Teddy, what's wrong with it?

Oh. It looks like a boy's coat when you wear it. And lots of boys wear pink.

Poor wee mite, he has three older sisters!

Neville, I said get up off the floor.

Who shot you dead?

David did? Well, I don't suppose he meant to. He may have meant to then, but he doesn't mean it now, and anyhow I say you can get up.

No, don't go and shoot David dead, because it's time to go home.

George. What did I tell you not to do? Well, don't do it.

And Sidney, don't wave that paint-brush about like that, you'll splash somebody. LOOK OUT, DOLORES!

Sidney! ... It's all right, Dolores, you aren't hurt, you're just surprised. It was only

It's all right, Dolores, you aren't hurt, you're just surprised.

a nice soft brush. But you'd better go and wash your face before you go home.

Because it's all blue.

Sidney, I saw you deliberately put that paintbrush up Dolores's little nostril.

No, it wasn't a jolly good shot. It was ... I don't want to discuss it, Sidney.

Now go and tell Dolores you're sorry.

Yes, now.

Thank you, Hazel, for putting the chairs straight for me.

You are a great helper.

Thank you.

And thank you, Dicky, for closing the cupboard door for me.

Dicky, is there somebody *in* the cupboard? Well, let her out at once.

What did you go into the cupboard for?

Are you all right, Peggy? What did you go into the cupboard for?

But we don't have mices – I mean mouses – in our toy cupboard. Mouses only go where there is food, and we don't have any food in our toy cupboard.

When did you hide a bicky in there?

Every day!

Well, perhaps we have got mices in our toy cupboard. I'll have to look.

No, you go and get your coat on.

Dicky – We never shut people in cupboards.

Because they don't like it.

What do you mean, she's puggy? Peggy's puggy?

Oh, she's got puggy hands. But you don't have to hold her hand . . .

Well, you must ask her nicely to let go.

Well, if she won't let go . . .

You'll have to work it out for yourself, Dicky.

Edgar and Timmy – your knitted caps are not for playing tug-of-war with. Look, now the pom-pom's come off.

Whose is it?

Well, give it back to Sidney.

Where are your caps?

Well, go and ask Sidney to give them back to you.

Turn round, Geoffrey. You've got your wellingtons on the wrong feet.

You've got your wellingtons on the wrong feet.

Yes, you have. You'll have to take them off and start again.

Why can't you reach?

Well, undo your coat and then you can bend. Take off your woolly gloves.

And your scarf.

You can keep your balaclava on. How many jerseys are you wearing?

Heavens. No wonder you can't bend.

Caroline, come and help Geoffrey.

Don't kick her, Geoffrey. She's come to help.

Sidney, I told you to put that paint-brush down ... LOOK OUT, DOLORES!

Well, *that* wasn't a very good shot, was it? You didn't mean to put it in her ear, did you?

Well, you shouldn't have.

You're all right, Dolores. It was just a bit of a surprise, but you'll have to go and wash again.

Because you've got a blue ear.

Sidney, I'm ashamed of you, a big boy of four, and she's only just three.

And Sidney, what have you done with Timmy and Edgar's caps?

No, I'm not going to guess.

And I don't want to know they are hidden in a special secret place, I want to know exactly where they are.

No, I'm not going to try and find them. You're going to tell me where they are.

Well, go and get them out of the waste-paper basket at once. Waste-paper baskets aren't for putting caps in.

Now go and say you are sorry to Dolores.

Yes, again.

We think his aggression is diminishing, but we do have setbacks.

Lavinia, is that your coat you've got on? It looks so enormous.

Oh, you're going to grow into it. I see.

Hazel, thank you for helping Betty into her jacket.

Just zip her up once. Not up and down.

No, Neville, you can't have a turn.

No, children, you can't all zip Betty.

Jenny, come here.

Jenny, when we have paid a visit to the littlest room, what do we do?

Jenny, when we have paid a visit to the littlest room, what do we do?

We pull our knickers up again.

Good-bye, Hazel, Good-bye, Bobbie. Good-bye, everybody.

Good-bye, Mrs Binton.

Hurry up, Sidney, because you'll keep your Mummy waiting.

Well, your Granny then.

Somebody is coming to take you away, aren't they, Sidney?

Good.

No, you won't see me tomorrow, Sidney. Tomorrow is Saturday, thank heaven.

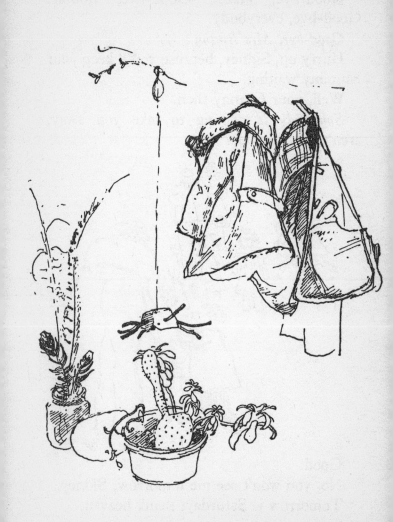

WRITER OF CHILDREN'S BOOKS

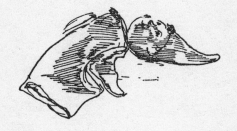

Writer of Children's Books

(The scene takes place in the book department of a large store, where an author has been auto- graphing copies; and now she is going to talk to her young readers.)

Hullo, boys and girls.

I was so pleased when you asked me to come along and tell you how I write my books for children.

Well, of course, the answer is – I don't. No, my books write themselves for me.

I think we are all Little Ones at heart, aren't we, grown-ups?

Yes, even the Growly Bear Daddys at the back!

And I don't believe I have ever grown up, and I think perhaps that's my secret. That, and the fact that kiddies come first with me.

Well, as you know, children, I write lots and lots of books for you, and this is how I set about it.

First of all I go upstairs to my Hidey-Hole – well, this is really just a great big upstairs work-room but I like to call it my Hidey-Hole.

I pin a notice on the door and it says, 'Gone to Make-Believe Land'. This is just my way of saying, 'Please don't come and bother me, because a book is writing itself for me, and we mustn't disturb it, must we?'

Then I put a clean white sheet of paper in

my typewriter, and I sit down in front of it, and I close my eyes.

And what do I see?

I see a rambling old house in Cornwall.

And I hear seagulls – and I see children – one – two – *three* children – scrambling up the cliffs, because they are very nearly late for tea.

And their names are Jennifer-Ann, and Robin-John, and the little one is called Midge – because he is the littlest one.

Oh yes, he has a proper name. It's Anthony Timothy Jeremy Michael, and he doesn't like porridge – but we won't tell anyone, will we?

And I sit there, and I type and I type, and as I do so I learn all about Jennifer-Ann's unruly mop of red curls, and her way with hedgehogs.

And about Robin-John, who is more of a fish than a boy – you should see him dive from the top diving-board.

And all about their father – kindly, over-worked, sunburned, twinkling Dr Merry-weather.

Then all of a sudden it's dinner-time, and I rub my eyes and I find myself back in my Hidey-Hole – and look! – a great pile of typed pages on the table beside me.

They must have written themselves while the story told itself to me.

And so I go on till a book is made.

And then I start another one.

This time it's a rambling old house in Yorkshire, and I hear sheep-bells, and I see children – three children – and their names are Sara-Mary, Jonathan-Christopher, and the little one is called Tiddler – because he is the littlest one.

It's always the same with me.

No, I never rewrite, and I never read what I have written.

But you children do, millions and millions of you children do, and that is my great joy.

And it is my husband's great joy, too.

He has given up his work to encourage me in mine.

We have made Hidey-Holes for each of our five children so that they, too, may learn to let books write themselves for them.

And my husband has his own Hidey-Hole – where he adds up.

Well, I think it is time I got back to my Hidey-Hole, don't you?

All Futura Books are available at your bookshop or
newsagent, or can be ordered from the following address:
Futura Books, Cash Sales Department,
P.O. Box 11, Falmouth, Cornwall TR10 9EN.

Please send cheque or postal order (no currency), and
allow 60p for postage and packing for the first book
plus 25p for the second book and 15p for each additional
book ordered up to a maximum charge of £1.90 in U.K.

B.F.P.O. customers please allow 60p for
the first book, 25p for the second book plus 15p per
copy for the next 7 books, thereafter 9p per book

Overseas customers, including Eire, please allow £1.25
for postage and packing for the first book, 75p for the
second book and 28p for each subsequent title ordered.

All titles listed are available in good bookshop or newsagents, or can be ordered direct from the following address:

Future Bookshop Readers Sales Department
P.O. Box 1, Falmouth, Cornwall TR10 9EN.

Please send cheque, postal order/international and allow 80p for postage and packing for the first book. Plus 20p for the second and 14p for each additional book ordered to a maximum charge of £2.00 in UK.

BFPO customers please allow 80p for the first book, 20p for the second book plus 14p per copy for the next 7 books, thereafter 8p per book.

Overseas Customers, including Eire, please allow £1.25 for postage and packing for the first book, plus 31p for each additional book.